I WONDER WHY...

Also by Shirley Burden

GOD IS MY LIFE

I WONDER WHY...

by Shirley Burden

DOUBLEDAY & COMPANY, INC.

GARDEN CITY, NEW YORK

I wonder why
some people
don't like me.

I like rain . . .

...and cool woods...

*...white snow
at Christmas...*

*...frost on
the window pane.*

I like clouds floating
in a blue sky…

...and birds...

...and cats...

...and little puppies.

I like the sea
when it wears diamonds...

...and castles...

*...and sand
when it squeezes
through my toes.*

I like flowers in spring...

…and lambs…

...God, and

angels with wings.

I like the smell
of burning leaves...

...and the taste
of juicy red apples...

*...pretty dresses
and weddings...*

...and babies.

I wonder why
some people
don't like me.